Ultimate Sticker Collection

How to use this book

Read the captions, then find
the sticker that best fits the space.
(Hint: check the sticker labels for clues!)

•

There are lots of fantastic extra stickers for
creating your own scenes throughout the book.

DK | Penguin Random House

Written by Beth Landis Hester
Edited by Elizabeth Dowsett and Helen Murray
Designed for DK by Lisa Robb
Cover designed by Lauren Rosier

First published in Great Britain in 2013 by
Dorling Kindersley Limited
80 Strand, London WC2R 0RL
A Penguin Random House Company.

10
019–182981–March/13

Page design copyright © 2013, 2018 Dorling Kindersley Limited.
DK, a division of Penguin Random House LLC.

LEGO, the LEGO logo, the Minifigure, and the Brick and Knob
configurations are trademarks of the LEGO Group.
All right reserved. © 2018 The LEGO Group
Manufactured by Dorling Kindersley, 80 Strand, London, WC2R 0RL,
under licence from the LEGO Group.

A CIP catalogue record for this book is available from the British Library.

ISBN: 978-1-4093-2549-9

Printed and bound in China

Discover more at
www.dk.com
www.LEGO.com

A WORLD OF IDEAS:
SEE ALL THERE IS TO KNOW

Meet the Friends

What's the best thing of all about Heartlake City? The amazing friends who live there, of course! Each of the girls is special and unique, but every single one is loyal, friendly and lots of fun. They are such good friends, they have even created a Friends Club to help others!

Emma

Emma photographs the things that inspire her. She uses her favourite colours and shapes to inspire new fashion designs!

Olivia

Clever Olivia loves to solve problems and discover new facts. In her workshop, she comes up with new inventions.

Stephanie

Sociable Stephanie loves helping out friends, and never forgets a birthday! As a Pet Patrol volunteer, she helps animals, too.

Andrea

Wherever there's a stage, Andrea will hop up and sing! She loves to perform for her biggest fans: her four best friends.

Mia

Mia has a way with animals and takes care of all her pets. At Heartlake Vet, she's also learning to care for other animals.

2

Ella

Ella loves riding, helping out at the stables and exploring horse trails in the woods – anything that involves horses!

Katharina

Look for Katharina at the stables. If she's not practising for her next big show, she may be grooming her favourite horse, Niki.

Nicole

Adventurous Nicole is the perfect companion for a camping trip or a hike! She loves exploring nature with friends.

Treehouse HQ

This is the Friends Club headquarters! It is fixed up as a girls-only hang-out for sunny days and starry nights.

3

Heartlake City

Heartlake City is a wonderful place to live. It has everything a girl could want! Olivia, Emma, Stephanie, Andrea and Mia are lucky to call it home. They always find lots of exciting places to visit and cosy spots to hang out. Start your tour here… then enjoy exploring!

Flying Club

Spread your wings at Heartlake City's Flying Club. Just a few exciting lessons and you'll soar up, up and away!

Heartlake Stables

Horseback riding is an exciting way to spend an afternoon. Visit the horses at the stables or take a trail ride!

Vet's office

This is where Sophie the vet cares for horses with sore hooves, lost puppies, and even a hedgehog with a cold!

Cruising

Who's ready for a road trip? Emma's car is a cool way to tour the coast or mountains near Heartlake City.

City Park Café

Take a snack break! The outdoor tables at City Park Café are a comfy place to catch up with friends.

Create your **own scene**

Fill this scene with the fun and exciting ways to spend time in Heartlake City.

©2018 LEGO

5

Olivia

Olivia is adventurous, smart and practical. And she's excited to meet new friends! She just moved to a beautiful new home in Heartlake City with her mum, dad and cat Kitty.

Budding scientist

Science is one of Olivia's favourite subjects. She loves to do experiments and figure out for herself how things work.

Olivia's diary

Olivia fills her diary with stories about her adventures and best friends. In Heartlake City, there is always something to write about!

Zobo the robot

Olivia has a talent for inventing. She built her pet robot herself! A remote control makes him go.

Anna

Olivia's mum is a kind, caring doctor. Her patients at the hospital love her almost as much as her family does!

Garden swing

This quiet spot is Olivia's favourite place to sit and think. There's no better perch for enjoying the beautiful garden.

6

Peter

Olivia's dad is a newspaper editor. He is also a great cook. He has a grill set up in the garden for delicious outdoor family meals.

Home sweet home

Peter, Anna and Olivia live in a big home with a pretty garden and roof terrace. Their address is 30 Heartlake Heights.

School work first

Olivia loves to learn new things. Her colourful desk is a cheerful spot to study her favourite school subjects: art, history and science.

Inventor's workshop

Olivia's microscope helps her see her experiments up close. She also has a workbench where she builds her latest inventions.

©2018 LEGO

Andrea

Outgoing Andrea was born to be a star! She loves sharing her talent for dancing, acting and especially singing. Andrea sings all the time – on stage, at work and even in the shower!

On stage

Bubbly Andrea is right at home in the spotlight. Her friends are there to cheer her on whenever she takes to the stage.

Singing star

Andrea dreams of singing for huge audiences. She's sure to be a superstar someday!

Piano practice

Playing piano takes hard work, but it's worth it! It's so much fun to be able to play all your favourite songs.

Bunny house

Andrea thinks that caring for animals is lots of fun – especially when they are as cute as her little bunny Jazz!

Stargazing

As well as wanting to be a star herself, Andrea also likes using her telescope to spot real stars in the night sky.

Tasty work

What's the best part of working at the café? Taste testing! Andrea gets to try every treat on the menu.

Serving food

At the café, Andrea's job is to bring the customers their drinks and snacks. But she always finds time to sing a little, too!

Carrot treat

Leftover food from the café makes a perfect snack for pets. This carrot goes right to the bunny house.

Building sand castles

The sounds of the waves and seagulls at the beach inspire some of Andrea's music… and her sand castles, too!

Emma

Emma has an eye for design. She keeps up with the latest trends and finds inspiration everywhere. She loves helping her friends add style to their lives. They love hearing her declare, "That's so you!"

Sweet treat

Emma enjoys a yummy milkshake from the café. A mix of two flavours is her one-of-a-kind blend.

Ready to ride

Emma is a champion horseback rider! She puts on her riding hat and is all set to go to a competition with her horse Robin.

Fashion designer

Emma mixes patterns and colours for original outfits. She measures each piece carefully so the fit is just right.

Drawing board

This style board lets Emma mix and match design ideas. She can rearrange the pictures until the outfit is perfect.

Happy snapper

Emma always keeps a camera handy to snap pictures around Heartlake City. You never know where creativity will strike!

10

Cool pool

This splash pool is a cool spot on hot days! Emma sits in the refreshing water to feel relaxed and chilled out.

Cute hedgehog

This spiky creature is well cared for by gentle Emma. Sometimes she even decorates him with bows, too!

Music to go

Emma loves to listen to music when she's out and about. Her MP3 player is loaded with all her favourite songs.

Computer research

Emma logs on to her laptop to find out about the latest fashion trends. There's always something new to learn!

11

Mia

Kind-hearted Mia loves animals. They seem to understand her when she talks to them! Mia is a vegetarian, which means she never eats meat, and she hopes to become a vet when she grows up.

Drum practice

Mia loves to drum! She always plays far away from the animals so they aren't frightened by the loud noise.

©2018 LEGO

Puppy kennel

Mia is a terrific animal trainer. Charlie's kennel is decorated with the ribbons he's won at the Heartlake City Dog Show.

©2018 LEGO

Budding vet

Mia helps out at the vet's office whenever she can. Mischievous puppy Scarlett has hopped on to the rescue trolley for a ride!

Sophie

Olivia's aunt is Heartlake City's top vet. She's teaching Mia how to care for all kinds of animals.

©2018 LEGO

©2018 LEGO

12

Bella

Mia's horse is a champion show jumper! Bella also loves to go for long runs with her favourite rider.

Favourite visitor

Mia visits Bella every morning and evening. She always has a kind word for her horse, and Bella loves to listen!

Tasty apple

Generous Mia is happy to share treats with all her animal friends. Bella's neighbour Niki will enjoy this crunchy apple!

Diary writing

In her journal, Mia writes about her adventures, her friends and her dreams of one day becoming a vet.

13

Stephanie

Mia's cousin Stephanie is lots of fun to be around. She is great at organising activities and cool parties! She knows just about everyone in Heartlake City and always has a bright smile for her many friends.

Looking good
Stephanie likes to have everything in its place, including well-brushed hair and cute accessories!

©2018 LEGO

Keen baker
Making cakes keeps Stephanie busy. When a friend has a birthday, she likes to treat them to something sweet!

Cute Coco
Stephanie's pet dog, Coco, is always carefully groomed. Plenty of brushing makes her fur shiny and soft.

©2018 LEGO

©2018 LEGO

Cool convertible
Stephanie can fit Coco and all her gear in this open-topped car. Now she'll turn on some tunes and hit the road.

©2018 LEGO

Celebration cake
Stephanie loves to party and to celebrate her friends. She brings along cake to get everyone in the party spirit!

14

Welcome to the Flying Club

This budding pilot can't wait for her next lesson. Watch overhead – the next plane you see might be Stephanie's!

Keep in touch!

This handwritten note is sure to bring a smile to one of Stephanie's many pen pals!

Grooming Niki

Stephanie always makes time for the horses at the stables. Her favourite horse, Niki, gets lots of attention!

Pet Patrol

Stephanie's knowledge of Heartlake City is a big help for the Pet Patrol. She'll get this lost pet home in no time!

15

Animal Friends

The Heartlake City friends look out for each other – and they take good care of animals, too! They have their own pets, but they are always on the look-out for other animals in need of rescue or help. Here are some of the fuzzy, feathered, and even spiny friends that the Heartlake girls love to spend time with.

Kitty
Olivia's mischievous cat finds lots of hiding places in her new Heartlake City home. Olivia always manages to find Kitty, though!

Caretakers
The girls work hard caring for their pets. Andrea sweeps out her bunny's house before school each day.

Robin
Emma always keeps her horse, Robin, groomed and pampered. Sometimes she decorates Robin's stable so even the hay is colour-coordinated!

Scarlett
This cute puppy has been well cared for by the girls. She even got a makeover! It's hard to believe she used to be scruffy.

Charlie
Charlie is a Heartlake City Dog Show champion! Proud Mia displays the awards at home on the kennel.

Goldie

Goldie had a broken wing when the girls found him near the treehouse. The friends helped nurse this bird back to health.

Maxie

This adorable cat has become a permanent resident of the treehouse! The girls even built Maxie a bed so she can sleep there.

Daisy

This bunny keeps the Pet Patrol on its toes! When Daisy hops away, Stephanie guides her home with a tasty carrot.

Oscar

There are all kinds of cute and cuddly creatures in Heartlake City. This is Oscar, the town's cutest – but not so cuddly – hedgehog!

©2018 LEGO

17

City Park Café

In the city park, there is a popular spot with a beautiful view of Lake Heart. This is where you'll find the busy café. With all the yummy treats on the menu and the sunny outdoor tables, it's easy to see why the friends love to hang out here!

Marie
Marie owns the café. She is an expert baker and a great boss. She greets guests with a smile and a fresh-baked treat.

Andrea the waitress
Working at the café, Andrea gets to see her friends and try all the food! Best of all, Marie lets her sing for the customers.

Cupcake
These are the café's speciality! Marie frosts each cupcake with care. Would you choose chocolate or strawberry?

Ker-ching!
The till holds all the day's earnings. When the café is busy, the money drawer fills up fast!

Delicious burger
Tasty sandwiches and burgers are the perfect lunch for hungry customers. There's one for every taste. Mia loves the veggie burger!

Busy baker
Marie starts baking early every morning. When customers arrive, the café is filled with the sweet smell of pies and cakes.

Cupcake offer!

The treat of the day is posted outside, where people walking by can see. Today's special is hard to resist!

Busy Andrea

As part of her job, Andrea takes the money from customers. She also brings food, tidies up and, of course, sings whenever she can.

Tidy Marie

Marie does the sweeping herself, since Andrea gets carried away singing and uses the broom as a microphone!

Super shakes

Marie is famous for her milkshakes! They are thick, creamy and delicious. And they come in everyone's favourite flavours.

Beauty Salon

For the latest fashions, everybody in Heartlake City goes to Butterfly Beauty Shop. The salon is the coolest place to get expert, personal advice on what will suit you best, whether it's a new accessory you're after or a whole new look. While you're there, why not indulge in some pampering, too?

Glamorous Emma

Emma is always on the look-out for pretty things. Her talent for design helps her spot the cutest fashions.

Style pro

Stylish Sarah works at the Beauty Shop. The girls love her design tips. She gives great advice about lipstick colours!

Pick and mix

There are so many cool accessories to choose from! Trying them on is the only way to see what looks best.

Chic sunglasses

What's the quickest way to add glamour to an outfit? Top it with a pair of sunglasses! The beauty shop has lots.

Hairdressing

Nobody can style hair like Sarah. Emma loves getting her hair done while Sarah shows her the latest styles.

Hair accessories

After a day of pampering, a pretty bow is the perfect finishing touch to any hairstyle.

20

Makeover mirror

When it's makeover time, the girls crowd around the mirror to admire each other's new looks.

New offers

The sign outside the shop promises the latest make-up ranges. Would you try this new petal-pink shade of lipstick?

Olivia's handbag

The pink trimming on Olivia's new handbag is a perfect match with her purple-and-pink outfit. What a great find!

Tool of the trade

A professional hairdryer gives Sarah's hairdos lots of shine and style.

At the Dog Show

With obstacle courses, judges to impress and a flower-filled stage, the annual dog show is one of Heartlake City's biggest events. It takes a lot of dedication and careful training to get a dog ready to compete, but it's lots of fun. The Heartlake girls love to take part with their dogs.

Mia the dog trainer

For Mia, the dog show is one of the highlights of the year. What could be better than an afternoon of animal fun?

Puppy bath

Each dog gets a good bath before going before the judges. Charlie's white coat looks best after a soak.

Pink ribbons

Pretty rosettes go to the dogs who perform best at the show. Mia is hopeful that her dog Charlie will win this one.

Grooming basket

Bows and a brush make sure the dogs look their best while they run, climb and jump through the obstacle course.

Trophy time!

The lucky winners stand on the podium of honour, alongside the dog show's grand-prize trophy.

Dog's dinner

The winning dogs get rosettes, but every dog earns a tasty bone to chew on. It is a dog's favourite prize of all!

...ye Outdoors

Where can you hike, swim, skate, ride and even fly? The best city around: Heartlake City! With beaches, mountains and pretty parks nearby, it's such an adventurous place to live. There are so many exhilarating activities, you'll find there's never a dull moment!

Home from home

This deluxe camper van is perfect for a few days holiday exploring further afield. Every night is a sleepover!

Healing hands

The girls found this poor bird who had a broken wing. Together, they nursed it back to health. Caring for living things makes them all feel good!

Barbecue

Who says dinner has to be inside? The girls love to cook meals al fresco on this outdoor grill.

Skater girl

Mia feels the breeze as she whizzes by on her skateboard. Her balance is so good, she can even hold an ice cream while she rides!

Secret stash

The girls hide their special collection of treasures, including crystals, in this box at the treehouse.

©2018 LEGO

I spy!

A telescope at the flight school lets Stephanie take a closer look at everything in the woods below and the sky above.

©2018 LEGO

Up, up and away!

Stephanie is learning to operate this high-flying prop plane. She can see all of Heartlake City from up here!

©2018 LEGO

©2018 LEGO

Cycling adventures

Nicole and Olivia bring a picnic on long bike rides. They can spend all day exploring the trails around Heartlake City!

Surf's up!

When the waves are high, a surfboard is one cool ride! Hop right on and catch a wave.

©2018 LEGO

Winter Fun

Winter is no reason to stay indoors in Heartlake City! Snowy days here give a whole new meaning to "cool". There are hills for sledding and skiing, and cosy fires for warming chilly toes. The whole city looks magical under a blanket of snow. How can you resist it?

Cosy clothes

The girls stay snuggly warm by bundling up! Olivia knows that lots of layers and a good pair of boots are key to keeping out the cold.

Hold tight!

At the first sign of snow, Olivia and her friends grab their sleds and start looking for the very best sledding hill.

Warming treat

After an active day outside, a cup of hot cocoa always hits the spot. Add marshmallows for a sweet topper!

Snowman

The girls love building snowmen. They use sticks to make the arms and top each snowman with a stylish hat.

Create your own scene

How would you spend a snow day? Fill this scene with any stickers you choose!

©2018 LEGO

©2018 LEGO

©2018 LEGO

At the Beach

Head to this sandy spot to catch a refreshing sea breeze. With the right gear, you might catch a cool wave, too! The beach has something for every mood. If you are looking for adventure, try the exciting water sports. Or if you want something more sedate, sink into the soft sand for a relaxing rest.

Surfer girl

Olivia has been practising her surfing all summer long. She paddles out, stands on her board and tries not to wipe out!

Seaside snack

Nicole remembers to bring along the picnic basket. Her favourite refresher on the beach? Orange juice!

Fun in the sand

This sand castle is fit for a princess! Four corner towers and a big pink flag give it an extra royal touch.

Out at sea

This powerboat zips through the waves with Olivia at the wheel. The blue windshield protects her from splashes.

Sun lounging

Olivia takes a break on her sun lounger. An umbrella shades it from the sun – it's always comfy and cool underneath!

Create your own scene

Are you ready to hit the beach? Fill the sand with seaside stickers to set the scene.

©2018 LEGO

©2018 LEGO

©2018 LEGO

©2018 LEGO

©2018 LEGO

©2018 LEGO

Riding Camp

The end of the school year means holidays, but for some lucky girls it also means the start of riding camp! The girls pack their bags and load their horses into the trailer. Then they are off for an unforgettable summer adventure of riding and learning to care for their horses.

Bon voyage!
The girls buckle up in this bus for the journey to camp. There is plenty of room for four girls and all their gear.

Pitching in
Stephanie grabs a pitchfork to prepare the stables. She spreads fresh hay on the floor to make a bed for each horse.

Theresa
Expert rider Theresa is the camp's head counsellor. She's a wonderful teacher, and great company, too!

Trail leader
Theresa leads the group on rides through the nearby pastures. She knows every trail by heart.

Grooming
Ella brushes her horse's mane, tail and coat to keep them healthy and shiny. Like the girls, the horses love to be pampered!

Tacking up

The girls learn how to fit a horse with a saddle and bridle. Once the tack is secure, Foxy is ready to go!

Fireside treats

After a day's riding, the campers chat around the fire, drink sweet cocoa and toast gooey marshmallows. Yum!

Helping out

Emma pushes a wheelbarrow to cart a bale of hay across camp. It's good exercise – and the horses will love it!

In class

Indoors, Theresa teaches the girls everything there is to know about riding and looking after horses.

At the Stables

Where do Heartlake City's horses live? Beautiful Heartlake Stables! The girls love to spend time here, grooming and petting their horses. They even like to decorate the horses' stalls to make them extra pretty. But the main event, of course, is taking the horses out for a ride!

Tasty carrot
Katharina is ready to ride! But first she offers her horse, Niki, a healthy snack to eat.

Horsey home
Bella loves her cosy stable – especially when Mia visits! Somehow Mia always seems to know what Bella needs.

Tea for two
Horseback riding can be tiring! A cup of tea or water after a ride helps the girls feel good as new.

Stable hand
At the stables, Mia does what she can to make sure the horses are comfortable and well fed.

Show jumping
Leaping over rails is a thrilling challenge. It looks like Katharina and her horse have mastered this one!

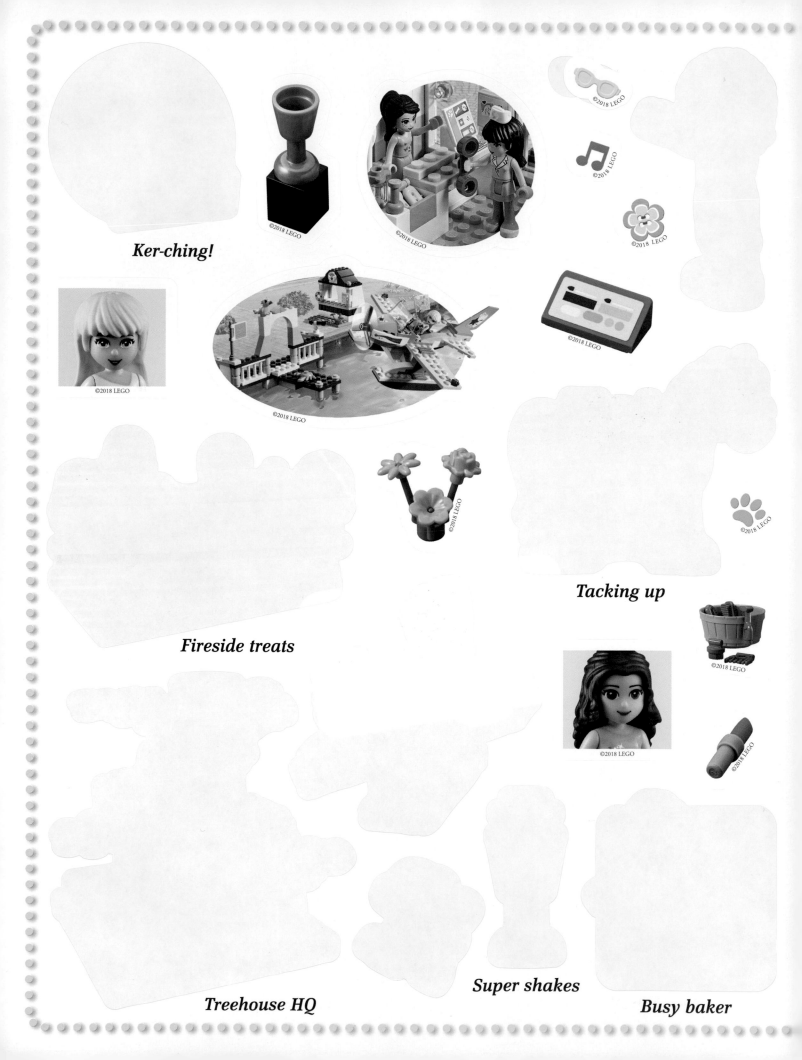

Ker-ching!

Fireside treats

Tacking up

Treehouse HQ

Super shakes

Busy baker

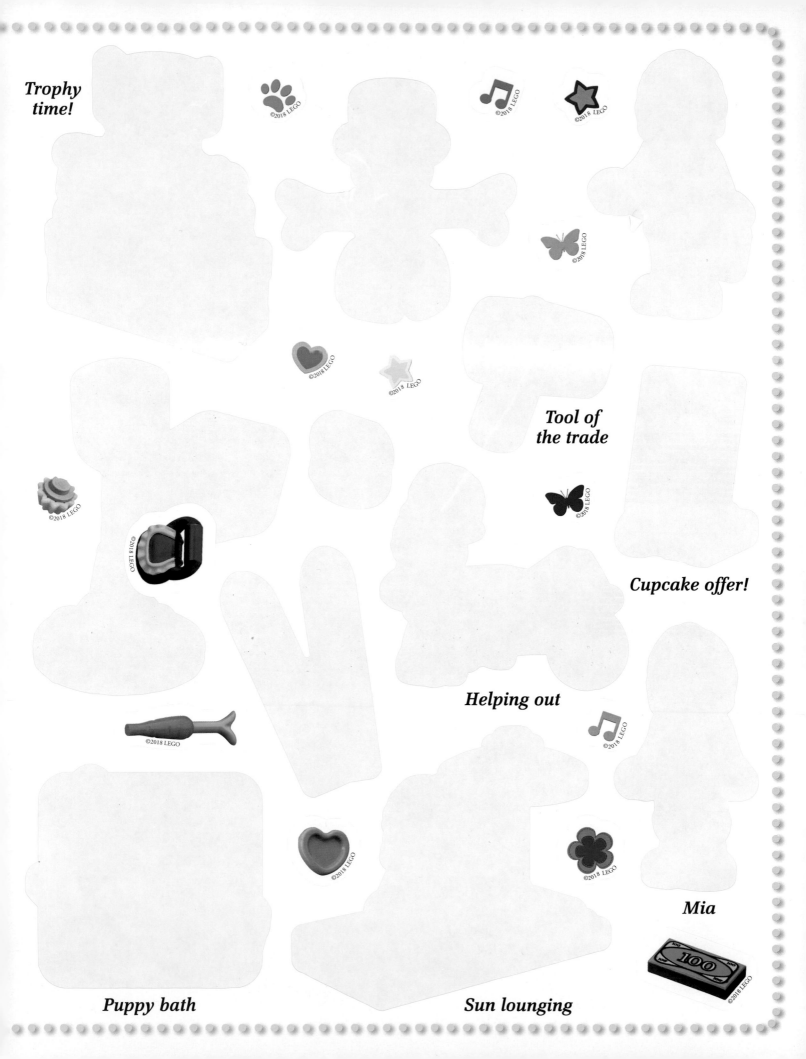

Trophy time!

Tool of the trade

Cupcake offer!

Helping out

Mia

Puppy bath

Sun lounging

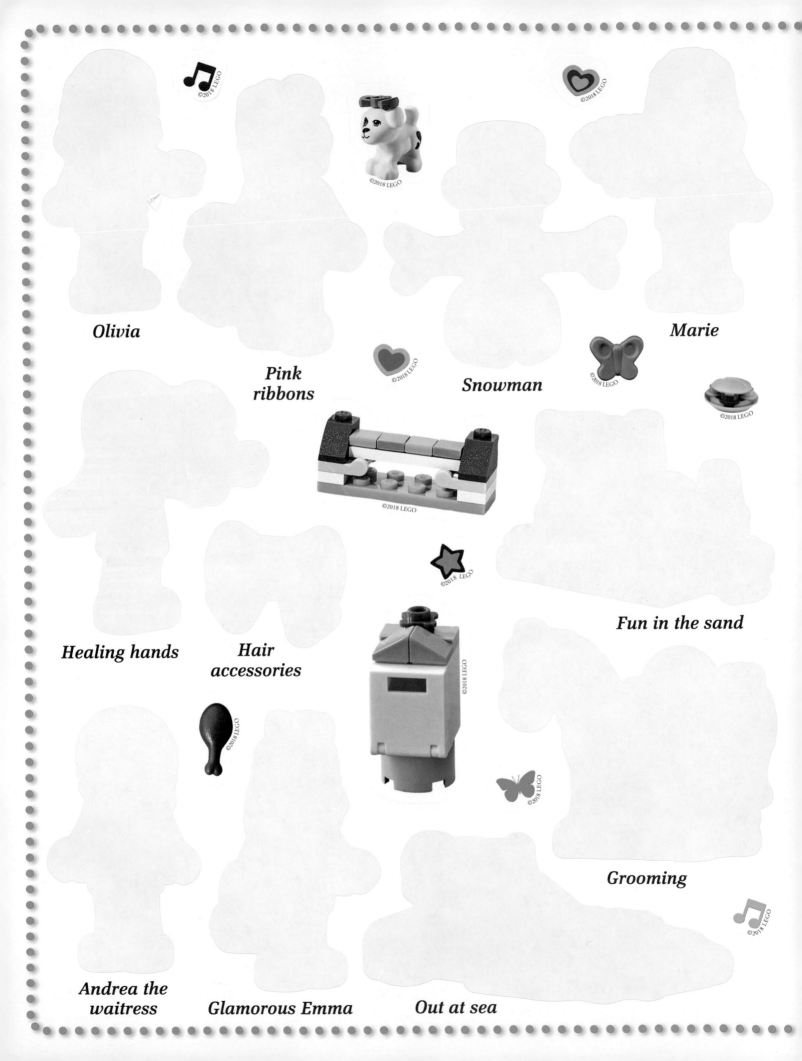

Olivia

Pink
ribbons

Snowman

Marie

Healing hands

Hair
accessories

Fun in the sand

Grooming

Andrea the
waitress

Glamorous Emma

Out at sea

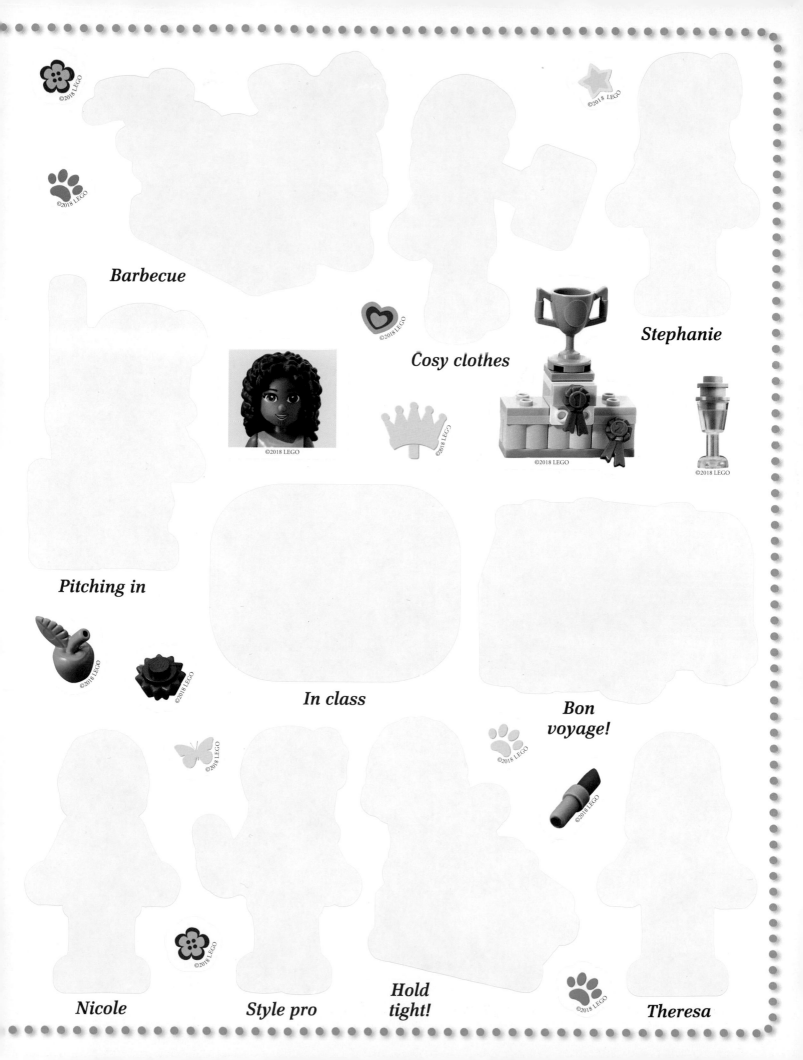

Barbecue

Cosy clothes

Stephanie

Pitching in

In class

Bon voyage!

Nicole

Style pro

Hold tight!

Theresa

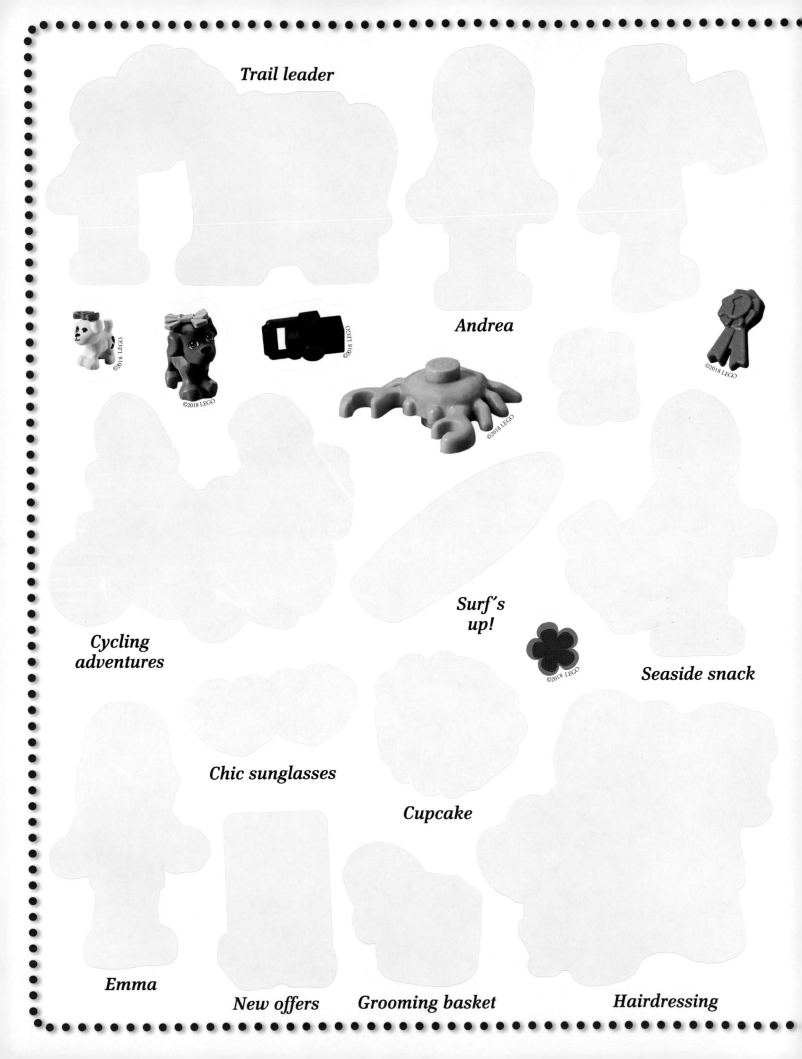

Trail leader

Andrea

Cycling
adventures

Surf's
up!

Seaside snack

Chic sunglasses

Cupcake

Emma

New offers

Grooming basket

Hairdressing

Dog's dinner

I spy!

Delicious
burger

Tidy
Marie

Busy Andrea

Mia the dog
trainer

Warming treat

Olivia's
handbag

Secret
stash

Ella

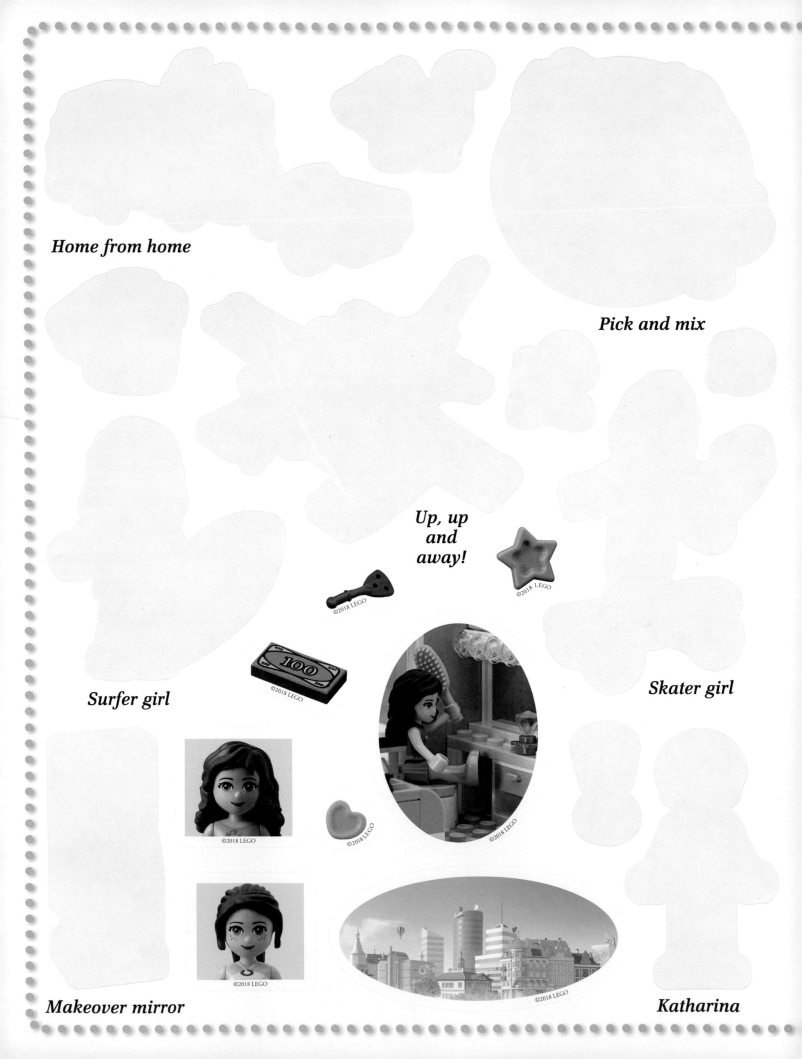

Home from home

Pick and mix

Up, up and away!

Surfer girl

Skater girl

Makeover mirror

Katharina

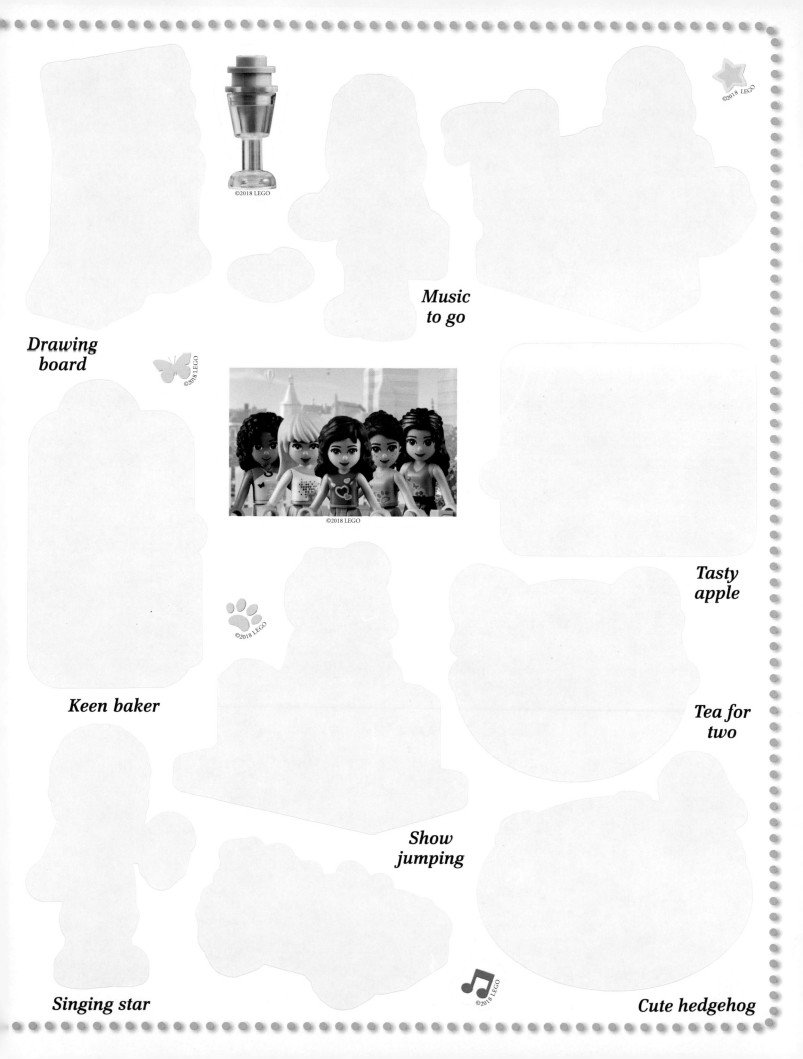

Music
to go

Drawing
board

Tasty
apple

Keen baker

Tea for
two

Show
jumping

Singing star

Cute hedgehog

©2018 LEGO

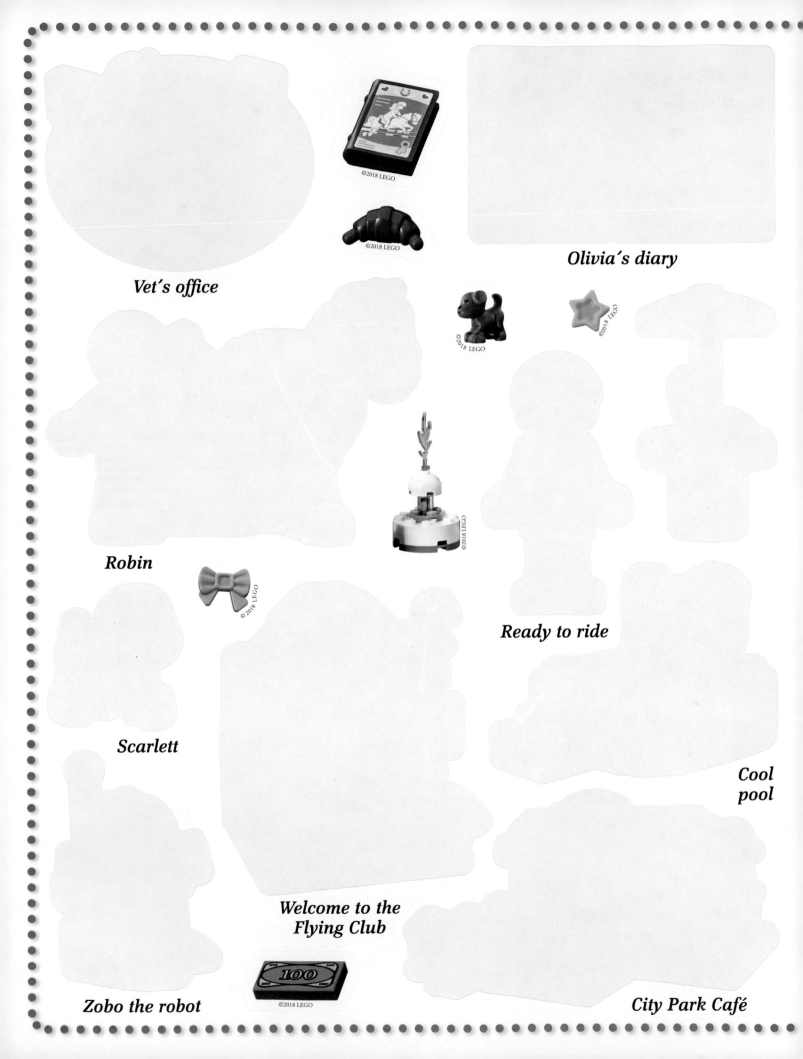

Vet's office

Olivia's diary

Robin

Ready to ride

Scarlett

Cool pool

Welcome to the
Flying Club

Zobo the robot

City Park Café

Stargazing

Pet Patrol

Fashion designer

Building
sand castles

Looking
good

Computer
research

Favourite
visitor

Flying Club

Drum
practice

Inventor's
workshop

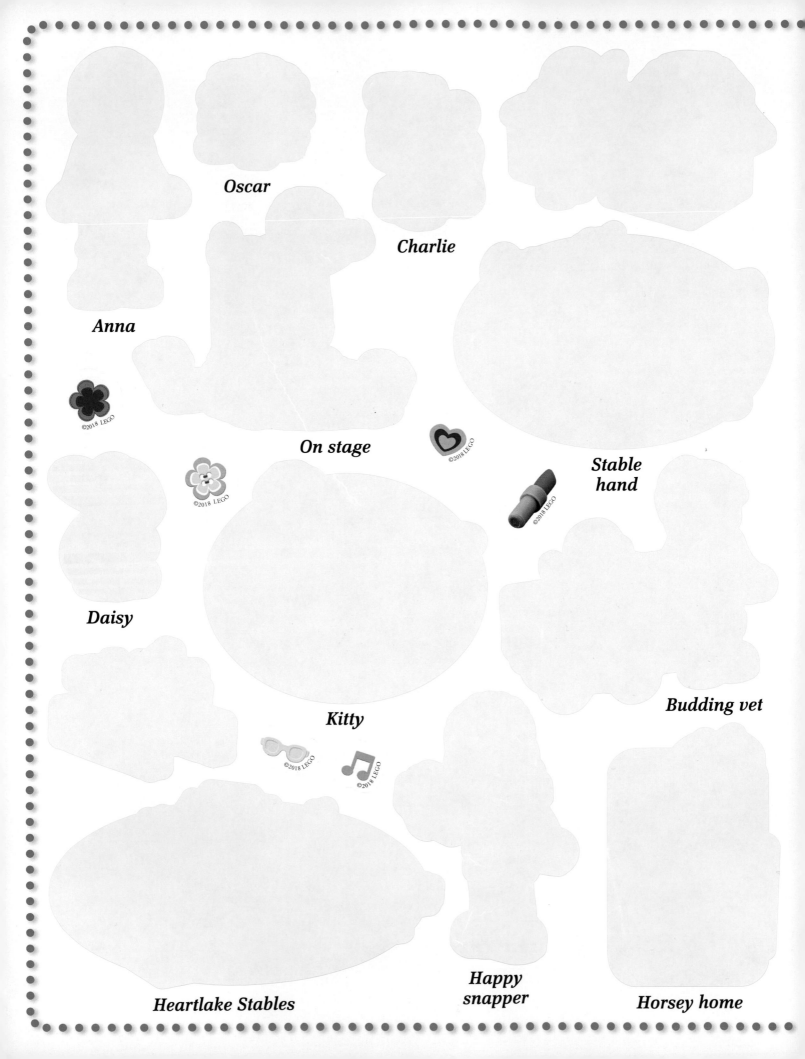

Oscar

Charlie

Anna

On stage

Stable hand

Daisy

Budding vet

Kitty

Heartlake Stables

Happy snapper

Horsey home

©2018 LEGO

©2018 LEGO

©2018 LEGO

©2018 LEGO

©2018 LEGO

©2018 LEGO

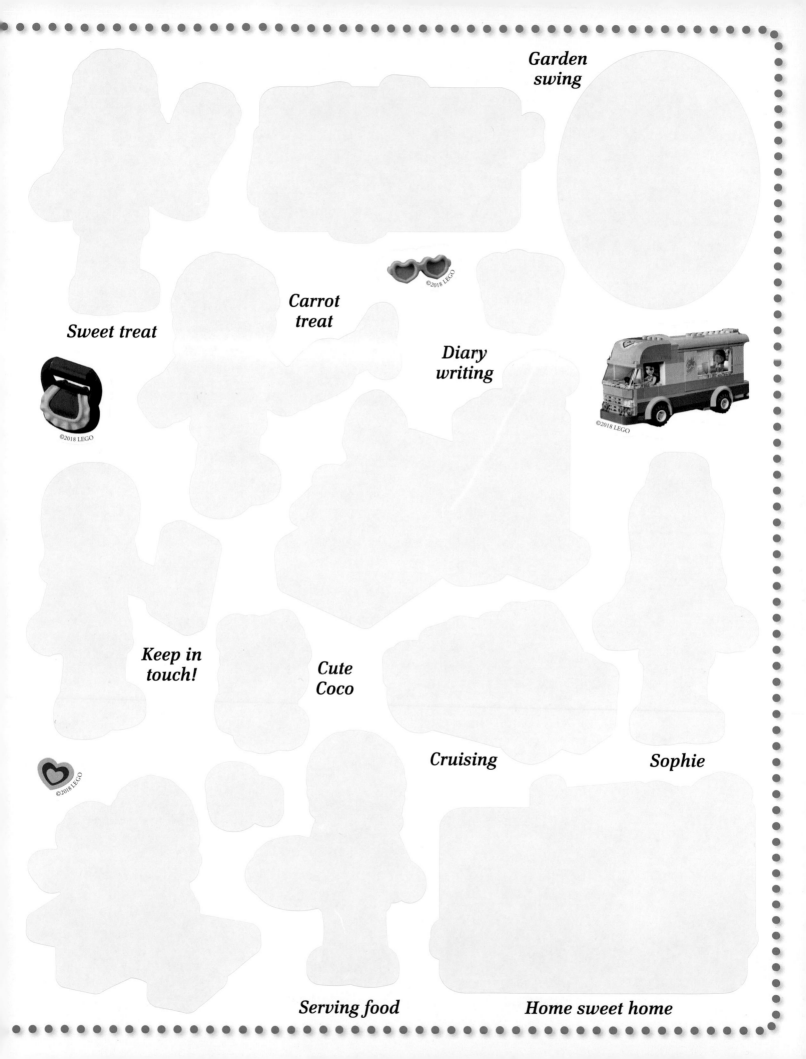

Garden
swing

Carrot
treat

Sweet treat

Diary
writing

©2018 LEGO

©2018 LEGO

Keep in
touch!

Cute
Coco

Cruising

Sophie

©2018 LEGO

Serving food

Home sweet home

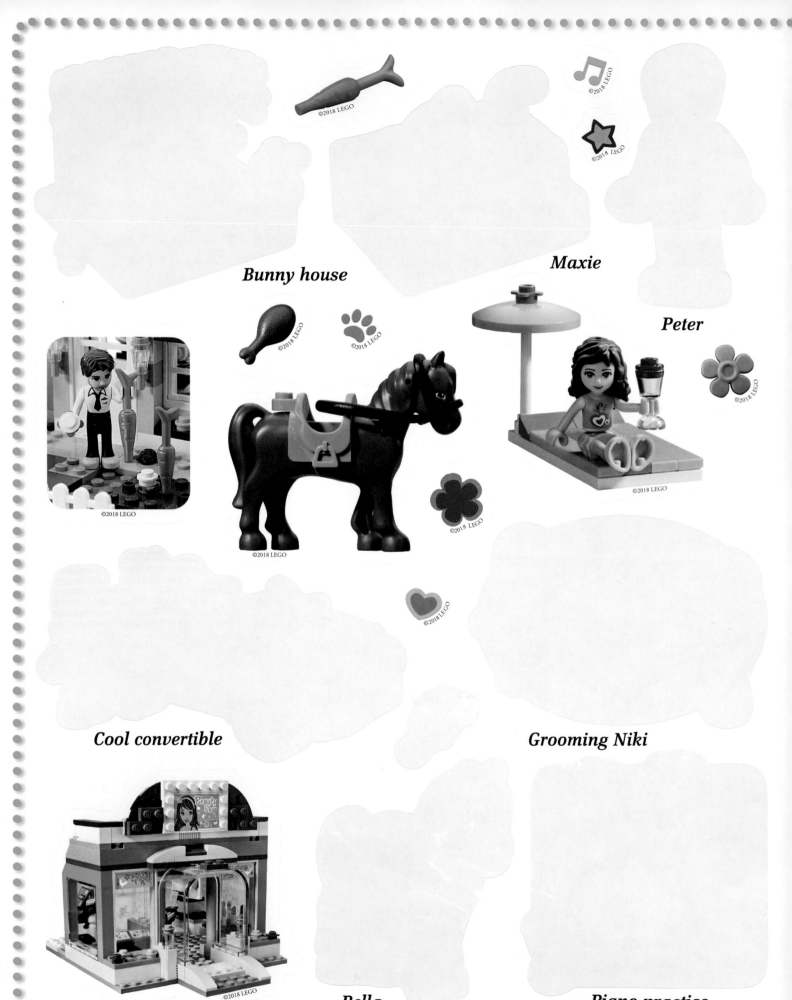

Bunny house

Maxie

Peter

Cool convertible

Grooming Niki

Bella

Piano practice

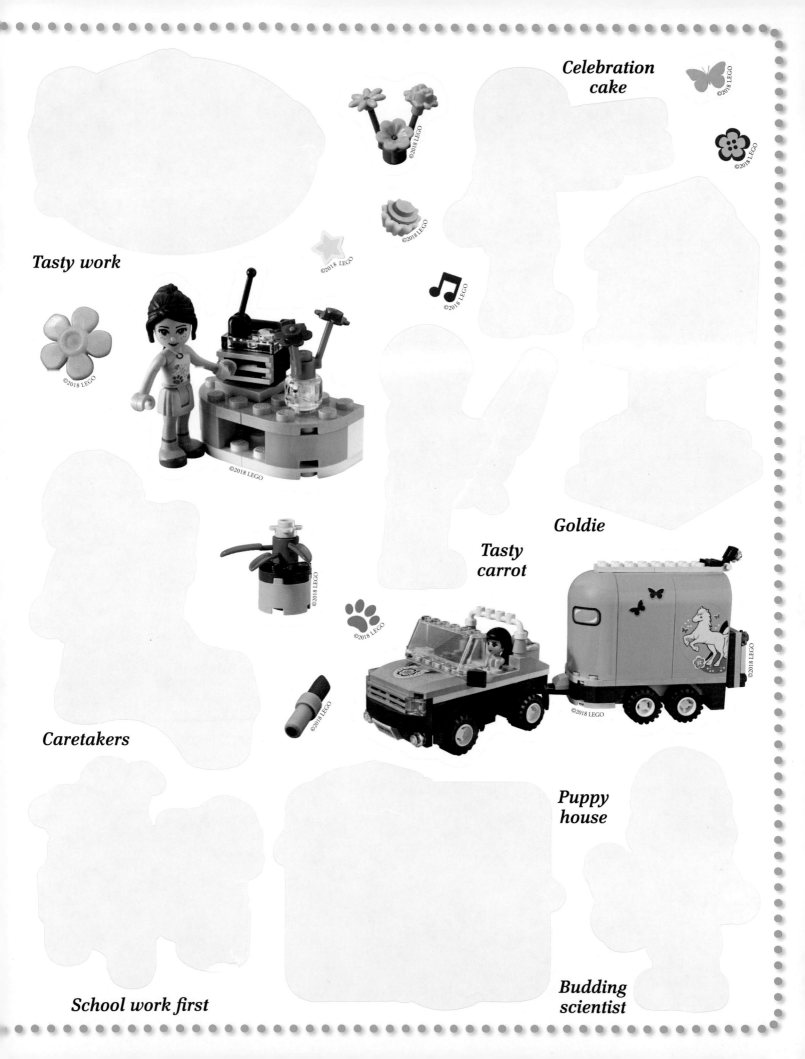

Celebration cake

Tasty work

Goldie

Tasty carrot

Caretakers

Puppy house

School work first

Budding scientist

Extra Stickers

Extra Stickers

©2018 LEGO

Extra Stickers

©2018 LEGO

Extra Stickers

©2018 LEGO

Extra Stickers

Extra Stickers

©2018 LEGO